HOFFNUNG'S CONSTANT READERS

By the author of:

THE MAESTRO

THE HOFFNUNG SYMPHONY ORCHESTRA

THE HOFFNUNG MUSIC FESTIVAL

THE HOFFNUNG COMPANION TO MUSIC

HOFFNUNG'S MUSICAL CHAIRS

HOFFNUNG'S ACOUSTICS

BIRDS, BEES AND STORKS

HOFFNUNG'S LITTLE ONES

HO HO HOFFNUNG

Hoffnung's
CONSTANT READERS

London
DENNIS DOBSON

Printed in Belgium by
Henri Proost & Co p.v.b.a.
Published by Dobson Books Ltd
80 Kensington Church Street, London W.8
ISBN 0 234 77703 6

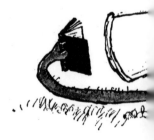

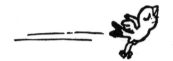

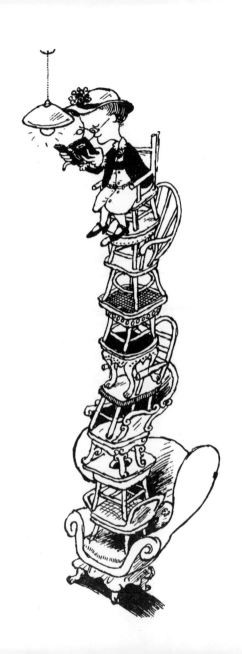